Riley & Milo

Thank you for
supporting our book!
Cassie

By Cassie L. D'Addeo, LMFT

@riley_and_milo_thebook

Published by Richter Publishing LLC www.richterpublishing.com

Editors: Haley Morton

Illustrator: Roger Luzardo

Copyright © 2021 Cassie D'Addeo

ISBN: 978-1-954094-07-9

DISCLAIMER

This book is designed to provide information on grief and loss only. This information is provided and sold with the knowledge that the publisher and author do not offer any legal or medical advice. In the case of a need for any such expertise, consult with the appropriate professional. This book does not contain all information available on the subject. This book has not been created to be specific to any individual's or organization's situation or needs. Every effort has been made to make this book as accurate as possible. However, there may be typographical and or content errors. Therefore, this book should serve only as a general guide and not as the ultimate source of subject information. This book contains information that might be dated and is intended only to educate and entertain. The author and publisher shall have no liability or responsibility to any person or entity regarding any loss or damage incurred, or alleged to have incurred, directly or indirectly, by the information contained in this book. You hereby agree to be bound by this disclaimer or you may return this book within the guarantee time period for a full refund. In the interest of full disclosure, this book contains affiliate links that might pay the author or publisher a commission upon any purchase from the company. While the author and publisher take no responsibility for the business practices of these companies and or the performance of any product or service, the author or publisher has used the product or service and makes a recommendation in good faith based on that experience. Characters appearing in this work are ficticous and do not resemble anyone living or deceased. The names of some characters have been changed to protect their identity. Any other resemblance to real persons, living or dead, is purely coincidental. This story is the opinion of the author and not that of the publisher

DEDICATION

To my nieces, Emilia Rae and Skylar Eve
and to my puppy, Riley Rue.

This is Riley and this is Milo

Riley and Milo were best friends.

They did everything together.

One day, Milo did not show up to puppy school. Riley was confused and worried.

Later that night, Riley found out Milo was in an accident. Milo was hurt and passed away.

Riley was shocked by the news. At first,
Riley could not believe that it was true.

For the next few days, Riley struggled
with eating her food, sleeping at night,
and even had bad dreams that she would
be in an accident.

Riley would get mad for no reason and scream..

"Life is not fair!"

When Riley went to the beach, she cried because she missed her best friend.

Riley even thought if she was a really good puppy, that Milo would come back. But that was not the case.

Milo's burial was tough but beautiful. Milo's owners buried him in his backyard right near his favorite banana tree.

The days went on and Riley's sadness continued to grow. Riley's family decided to bring her to a counselor to talk about the death of her best friend.

Riley went to counseling for a few weeks.
She learned that it was okay to feel sad,
confused and even mad at times.

...he best ways of ...ing the things ...ng together.

Sometimes, Riley would still feel sad.
When she did, she visited Milo's banana tree.

Riley also learned other coping strategies in counseling, things she could do when she felt sad to make her feel better.

Riley asked her counselor, "Where did Milo go?"
The counselor explained that depending on what you
believe in, some dogs go to doggy heaven, others simply
rest in the ground and some go to the moon.

Riley found comfort that Milo was
running around on the moon.

Within a few months, Riley started to feel better. She still missed Milo greatly but understood that it was okay and normal to feel that way.

On the nights that Riley missed Milo the most,
Riley would go to the beach with her family
just to look at Milo's moon.

A Message to Parents and Caregivers:

Processing death with a child is not an easy task. In fact, many people find it overwhelming and do not know how to initiate the conversation with young children. Using books, or bibliotherapy, as a method of explaining loss and grief is an effective tool for complex conversations. The book Riley and Milo leads young readers through the stages of grief such as: denial, anger, bargaining, sadness and acceptance. As the puppy Riley is processing the death of her best friend Milo, she explains her feelings and the impact of Milo's death on her life. This book was created to help naturalize the emotions and experiences of young readers who are coping with grief and loss.

When processing death with a child, it is important to explain the death using honest and basic facts. Caregivers can also name feelings to help the young child label his or her emotions. Using visuals, such as an emotion chart like the one Riley used in counseling, is another effective tool for identifying the emotion that the child is currently experiencing.

Typically, young children have many misconceptions or even fears about death. Fostering an environment of non-judgmental open communication helps mitigate these fears and anxieties associated with the loss. Some children may express a multitude of questions while others may present as quiet and reserved. In either situation, caregivers should answer questions in truthful yet simple terms.

The internal stress that children experience during a loss can affect social, emotional, behavioral, and academic functioning. Changes that may occur in young children are sleep disturbances, loss of appetite, anger outbursts, loss of interest in activities, regression to an earlier developmental stage, drop in academic performance or newly developed fears. If symptoms persist, professional assistance may be needed. A child and adolescent psychotherapist, psychologist, school social worker or school counselor can help the child process the death or support the family with obtaining professional services in the community.

Respectfully,

Cassie L. D'Addeo, LMFT
Child & Adolescent Psychotherapist
Owner, Green Couch Counseling, LLC

Emotion Board

Silly

Sad

Angry

Nervous

Playful

Happy

Surprised

Scared

Confused

About the Author

Cassie D'Addeo is a Licensed Marriage and Family Therapist. Her professional interests and clinical experience focus on relationship issues, family and parenting challenges, work-life balance; stress, anxiety and mood management; self-esteem, and grief counseling. She strives to create a warm, non-judgmental environment in which clients feel understood and comfortable exploring issues, while cultivating self-awareness and coping skills as they embark upon the journey to create positive change.

She received a Bachelor of Arts degree in Legal Studies (Quinnipiac University, CT), a Master of Science degree in Marriage and Family Therapy (Nova Southeastern University, FL) and a PEL Endorsement in School Counseling (National Louis University, IL). Her previous clinical experience includes outpatient, residential, home-based therapy, and school-based counseling. At Green Couch Counseling, LLC, she works with children as young as three, adolescents, adults, and families, using a variety of clinical approaches including cognitive-behavioral, solution focused, and family systems. When working with children and teens, Cassie always welcome family participation in the clinical process.

CPSIA information can be obtained
at www.ICGtesting.com
Printed in the USA
LVRC080903260521
688188LV00034B/609